MUSICAL MEMORIES

OF TIN PAN ALLEY, BROADWAY & HOLLYWOOD

Arranged for
PIANO/VOCAL/GUITAR/ORGAN

Edited by
IRVING BROWN

chappell music company

Book Design by **LEE SNIDER**

Production Assistant **DENNIS O'DONNELL**
Music Arranger **FRANK METIS**

Contents

MUSICAL MEMORIES

OF TIN PAN ALLEY, BROADWAY & HOLLYWOOD

The world and its trends change continually but there are many great traditions which stand the test of time. The mainstay of American popular music has always been the romantic love song and the ballad was its old and well-beaten path. And some of these songs do not seem to perish. They live on. They are revived by the dedicated and they are rediscovered by the young. And they seem to gather deeper meaning and resonance with each renaissance. They are cherished because they stir deep memories and harbor lovely sentiments.

In this book there are songs of an emotional nature, such as the haunting "Try to Remember" (from THE FANTASTICKS) and the stirring "Theme from EXODUS" (from the movie which starred Paul Newman). They display a kind of music which is expansive in melodic design and rich in harmonic structure. They uphold a tradition which has persisted from early operetta to the modern musical comedy (a tradition quite opposed to sounds of city life being reproduced as melody and rhythm). The musical comedy songs of Lerner and Loewe, for example, searched out new and fresh ways of expressing the romantic nature. GIGI, CAMELOT, MY FAIR LADY. And we may remember the star performers so closely associated with their songs through stage and film: Leslie Caron, Louis Jourdan, Maurice Chevalier. Richard Burton and Julie Andrews. Rex Harrison with Julie Andrews and Audrey Hepburn.

The songs in this book are songs which saw Americans through world wars and a depression and discontent. They encompass Lindbergh's solo flight and the SST. In the face of many harsh realities these melodies held up a charming and fragrant illusion. They evoke memories which comprise the early musical hit, GOOD NEWS by DeSylva, Brown and Henderson, and the later Broadway world of Jule Styne's BELLS ARE RINGING, GYPSY, and FUNNY GIRL — shows which have starred performers like Judy Holliday, Ethel Merman, and Barbra Streisand.

Many of these songs emanated from Tin Pan Alley, the fabled street which spanned Broadway's Great White Way and Hollywood. Some were the rage during the heyday of radio's golden age and some achieved popularity through motion pictures. "You're the Cream in My Coffee" was published in 1928; and "May I" is from the Bing Crosby film LOVE THY NEIGHBOR.

Perhaps Tin Pan Alley was always a state of mind — vigorous, creative and daring. Song writers and other musical artists could always come up with techniques and methods for making hits and setting trends. At its most sophisticated, the search was not only for a new tune but for a musical abandon, a stunning freshness, an expressive dash, a lyrical agility. The music was designed to catch the ear as well as the heart of the public.

And to be sure, the songs in this book bespeak an innocence — a naivete with a slight hint of irony — while they sustain the fragrance of youth and love. There's the sauciness of a Cole Porter lyric "C'Est Magnifique" from CAN-CAN, the wistful fancy of Mack Gordon and Harry Revel's "Did You Ever See a Dream Walking?", the loving devotion of Kurt Weill's "Here I'll Stay."

And so, from Tin Pan Alley and the time of the lavish Ziegfeld Follies, from the Jazz Age to the Swing era of the big bands, from the musical comedy theatre and the Hollywood sound stage, from the intimate night club revue, here are enduring songs that speak of tenderness and feeling and the thrill of passion — and which give a touch of glamor to the beholder. They will continue to endure because they have the power to stir memory and provoke timeless sentiments . . . and so, we have the musical memories of Tin Pan Alley, Broadway and Hollywood.

A PHOTO GALLERY of
Tin Pan Alley, Broadway & Hollywood's Great Songwriters

MACK GORDON
& HARRY REVEL

BETTY COMDEN & ADOLPH GREEN

B. G. DESYLVA, LEW BROWN, RAY HENDERSON

STEPHEN SONDHEIM   COLE PORTER

ALAN JAY LERNER & FREDERICK LOEWE

ARTHUR SCHWARTZ

JULE STYNE

TOM JONES & HARVEY SCHMIDT

HAROLD ROME

BURTON LANE

KURT WEILL

ROBERT WRIGHT & GEORGE FORREST

SONNY BOY

Music & Lyrics by AL JOLSON,
B.G. DeSYLVA, LEW BROWN and RAY HENDERSON

heav - en   for   me right here on earth!   And then the
poco rit.

I'm   old and   gray,   dear,   Prom - ise you won't
an - gels grew lone - ly, Took you 'cause they're
a tempo

stray,   dear,___   I   love you   so,   Son - ny
lone - ly, Now I'm lone - ly too, Son - ny

Boy.___
Boy.___

molto rall.

AN ORCHID TO YOU

Music & Lyrics by
MACK GORDON and HARRY REVEL

IF IT'S THE LAST THING I DO

Music & Lyrics by
SAMMY CAHN and **SAUL CHAPLIN**

TILL

Lyrics by CARL SIGMAN

Music by CHARLES DANVERS

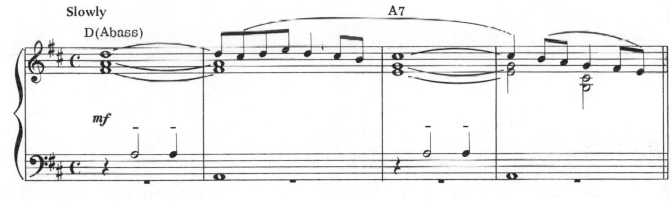

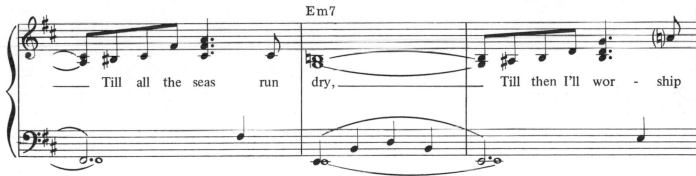

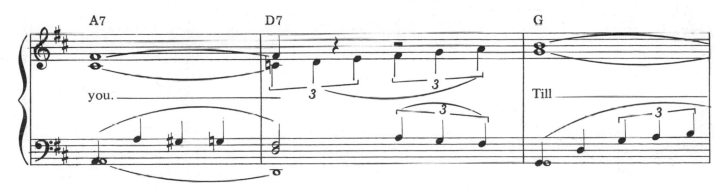

AS LONG AS I LIVE

Lyrics by MACK GORDON

Music by HARRY REVEL

A BOY AND A GIRL WERE DANCING

Lyrics by MACK GORDON

Music by HARRY REVEL

(HERE AM I) BROKENHEARTED

Music & Lyrics by B. G. DeSYLVA,
LEW BROWN and RAY HENDERSON

The last time that we said "good-bye," I knew that she was

through, It's bad e-nough that I lost her, I had to lose him

too. There they go___ in their joy,___ Hap-py girl,___

luck-y boy,___ And here am I___ Bro-ken

Heart - ed. ed.

I PLAYED FIDDLE FOR THE CZAR

Lyrics by MACK GORDON

Music by HARRY REVEL

IT WAS SO BEAUTIFUL

Lyrics by ARTHUR FREED

Music by HARRY BARRIS

LITTLE PAL

Music & Lyrics by AL JOLSON, B. G. DeSYLVA,
LEW BROWN and RAY HENDERSON

MY SIN

Music & Lyrics by B. G. DeSYLVA,
LEW BROWN and RAY HENDERSON

NEVERTHELESS

Music & Lyrics by
BERT KALMAR and HARRY RUBY

A STAR FELL OUT OF HEAVEN

Music & Lyrics by
MACK GORDON and HARRY REVEL

(THAT'S JUST MY WAY OF) FORGETTING YOU

Music & Lyrics by B. G. DeSYLVA,
LEW BROWN and RAY HENDERSON

get-ting You. _____ If I gave my-self the time to think a-

bout you, I'd go mad to think that I'm with-

out you. Each night now I pray that I

may find a way, Find a way of For - get - ting

You. _____ If You. _____ If

49

TOGETHER

Music & Lyrics by B.G. DeSYLVA,
LEW BROWN and RAY HENDERSON

YOU TRY SOMEBODY ELSE

Music & Lyrics by B.G. DeSYLVA,
LEW BROWN and RAY HENDERSON

AT LONG LAST LOVE

Music & Lyrics by
COLE PORTER

this feel - ing of joy, _____ Or is what I feel the real Mc - Coy? _____ Is it for all time, _____ or sim - ply a lark? _____ Is it Gra - na - da I see or

BUTTON UP YOUR OVERCOAT

Music & Lyrics by B. G. DeSYLVA,
LEW BROWN and RAY HENDERSON

THE BEST THINGS IN LIFE ARE FREE

Music & Lyrics by B. G. DeSYLVA,
LEW BROWN and RAY HENDERSON

BY MYSELF

Lyrics by HOWARD DIETZ

Music by ARTHUR SCHWARTZ

C'EST MAGNIFIQUE

Music & Lyrics by
COLE PORTER

*Pronounced "say man-yee-feekuh"

GOOD FOR YOU - BAD FOR ME

Music & Lyrics by B. G. DeSYLVA,
LEW BROWN and RAY HENDERSON

GOOD NEWS

Music & Lyrics by B. G. DeSYLVA,
LEW BROWN and RAY HENDERSON

EVERYTHING'S COMING UP ROSES

Lyrics by STEPHEN SONDHEIM

Music by JULE STYNE

HERE I'LL STAY

Lyrics by ALAN JAY LERNER

Music by KURT WEILL

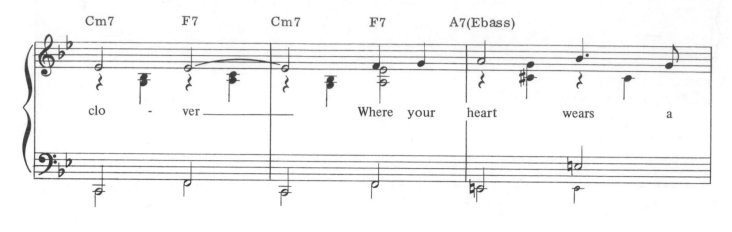

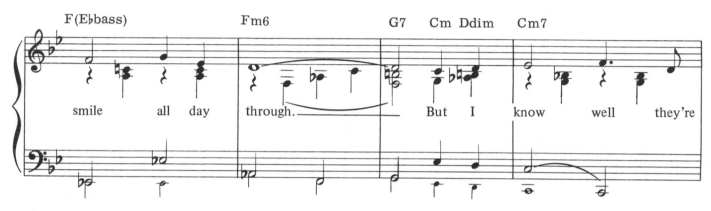

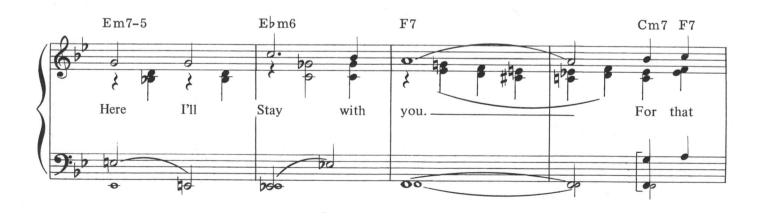

HOW DO YOU SPEAK TO AN ANGEL?

Lyrics by BOB HILLIARD

Music by JULE STYLE

I HATE TO THINK THAT
YOU'LL GROW OLD BABY

Music & Lyrics by
LEW BROWN and RAY HENDERSON

I LOVE PARIS

Music & Lyrics by
COLE PORTER

Par - is in the win - ter when it driz - zles,

Fm   G7   Cm

I   Love   Par - is in the sum - mer when it siz - zles.

C

I   Love   Par - is ev - 'ry mo - ment,_____

f

                                    C(E bass)   E♭dim

_____   Ev - 'ry   mo - ment of the

I SEE YOUR FACE BEFORE ME

Lyrics by HOWARD DIETZ

Music by ARTHUR SCHWARTZ

89

I TALK TO THE TREES

Lyrics by ALAN JAY LERNER

Music by FREDERICK LOEWE

el - se's heart - - strings too.

I tell you my dreams, And while you're

lis - t'ning to me I sud - den - ly see them

come true. I can see us on an

come true.

IF EVER I WOULD LEAVE YOU

Lyrics by ALAN JAY LERNER

Music by FREDERICK LOEWE

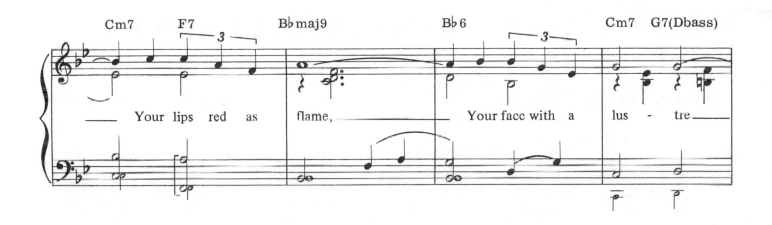

Your lips red as flame, ____ Your face with a lus - tre

____ that puts gold to shame! ____ But if I'd ev - er leave you, ____

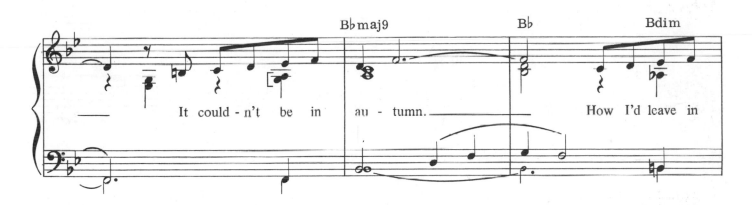

____ It could - n't be in au - tumn. ____ How I'd leave in

au - tumn I nev - er will know. ____ I've seen how you

I'M FLYING HIGH

Music & Lyrics by B. G. DeSYLVA,
LEW BROWN and RAY HENDERSON

I WANT TO BE BAD

Music & Lyrics by B. G. DeSYLVA,
LEW BROWN and RAY HENDERSON

I'VE GOT TO PASS YOUR HOUSE TO GET TO MY HOUSE

Music & Lyrics by LEW BROWN

Cm

your house _____ to get to my house. _____ I

C   G7(Dbass)   C7

swear I'll move a - way, _____ But then the next

Fm   Ab7(Gbbass) 3   G7   3

day _____ I wake up and say _____ She may change her

Fm   3   Cm   3

mind, _____ I guess that I'll stay, _____ I'm fun - ny that

Fm6   G7   3   Cm

way, _____ I'm fun - ny that way. _____

sfz

I'VE GROWN ACCUSTOMED TO HER FACE

Lyrics by ALAN JAY LERNER

Music by FREDERICK LOEWE

smiles, her frowns, her ups, her downs are sec - ond
joys, her woes, her highs, her lows are sec - ond

na - ture to me now,   Like breath - ing
na - ture to me now,   Like breath - ing

out and breath - ing in.   I was se -
out and breath - ing in.   I'm ver - y

rene - ly in - de - pen - dent and con - tent be - fore we met,
grate - ful she's a wom - an and so eas - y to for - get,

JUST IN TIME

Lyrics by BETTY COMDEN & ADOLPH GREEN

Music by JULE STYNE

JUST IMAGINE

Music & Lyrics by B. G. DeSYLVA,
LEW BROWN and RAY HENDERSON

LET ME ENTERTAIN YOU

Lyrics by STEPHEN SONDHEIM

Music by JULE STYNE

LIFE IS JUST A BOWL OF CHERRIES

Music & Lyrics by
LEW BROWN and *RAY HENDERSON*

LOST IN THE STARS

Lyrics by MAXWELL ANDERSON

Music by KURT WEILL

LOVE IS A DANCING THING

Lyrics by HOWARD DIETZ

Music by ARTHUR SCHWARTZ

When this en-tranc-ing thing____

Came like a spring song, I heard the sing-song of it.

Love Is A Danc-ing Thing,____ Ro-

manc-ing my light heart a-way.

1.
light heart a-way.

2.
light heart a-way.____
ritard.

LUCKY IN LOVE

Music & Lyrics by B. G. DeSYLVA,
LEW BROWN and *RAY HENDERSON*

I don't mind that at po-ker I'm green,___ If I
I won't mind that at po-ker I'm green,___ If my

stand ace high with a beau-ti-ful queen!___
king of hearts on-ly takes in his queen!___

I'll say I'm Luck-y In Love, If you take me,

that-'ll make me oh, so Luck-y In Love.

LONG BEFORE I KNEW YOU

Lyrics by BETTY COMDEN and ADOLPH GREEN

Music by JULE STYNE

and felt this glow. But now you real - ly are here and now at last I know That Long Be - fore I Knew You I loved you so. so.

MAKE SOMEONE HAPPY

Lyrics by BETTY COMDEN and ADOLPH GREEN

Music by JULE STYNE

One face that lights when it nears you,
One { man / girl } you're ev - 'ry - thing to.
Fame, __ if you win it, Comes and goes __ in a min - ute.
Where's the real __ stuff in life to cling to?
Love __ is the an - swer,

MY CUP RUNNETH OVER

Lyrics by TOM JONES

Music by HARVEY SCHMIDT

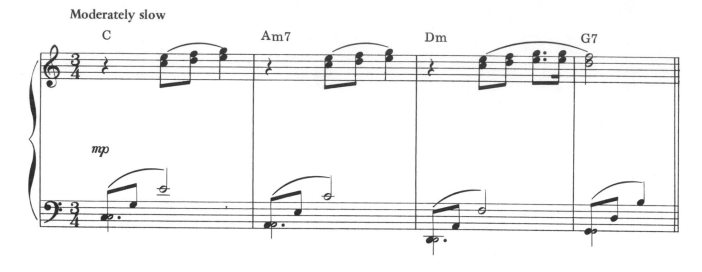

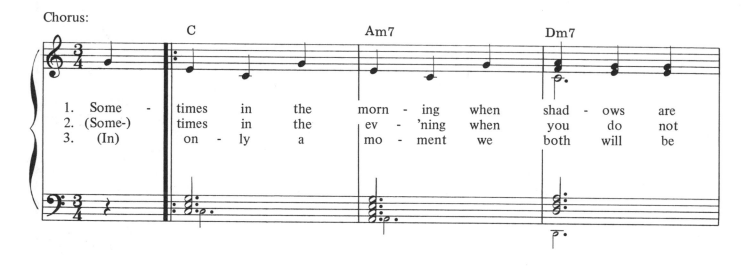

Chorus:

1. Some - times in the morn - ing when shad - ows are
2. (Some-) times in the ev - 'ning when you do not
3. (In) on - ly a mo - ment we both will be

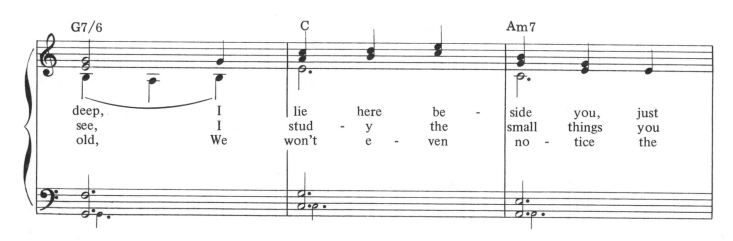

deep, I lie here be - side you, just
see, I stud - y the small things you
old, We won't e - ven no - tice the

MY LUCKY STAR

Music & Lyrics by B. G. DeSYLVA,
LEW BROWN and RAY HENDERSON

signed My Luck - y Star,_____ There

must have been a hol - i - day._____

Why can't I be as

oth - ers are _____ Whose lives are like the

MY SONG

Music & Lyrics by
LEW BROWN and RAY HENDERSON

much of Franz Schu - bert's touch, And
I can't be - gin with Irv - ing Ber -
lin. My Song,_____ though a po - et would
nev - er o - kay,_____ My Song,_____

ON A CLEAR DAY (YOU CAN SEE FOREVER)

Lyrics by ALAN JAY LERNER

Music by BURTON LANE

Moderately slow

OOH, I'M THINKING

Music & Lyrics by
LEW BROWN and RAY HENDERSON

whole day through, but Ooh, I'm Think - ing,

Ooh, I'm Think - ing of the things that we could

doo - oo! I've got the pic - ture clear in my im -

ag - i - na - tion, dear, You're in my arms, the

THE PARTY'S OVER

Lyrics by BETTY COMDEN & ADOLPH GREEN

Music by JULE STYNE

PEOPLE

Lyrics by BOB MERRILL

Music by JULE STYNE

SMALL WORLD

Lyrics by STEPHEN SONDHEIM

Music by JULE STYNE

Soon It's Gonna Rain

Lyrics by TOM JONES

Music by HARVEY SCHMIDT

STRANGE MUSIC

Music & Lyrics by
ROBERT WRIGHT and GEORGE FORREST
Based on a melody by Edvard Grieg

THANK YOUR FATHER

Music & Lyrics by B. G. DeSYLVA,
LEW BROWN and RAY HENDERSON

ressed them from a - bove. _____

And   thank
Though   your

good - ness for their mar - riage, And for that ba - by
fa - ther's name was Stan - ley, Thank good - ness he was

car - riage!
man - ly!   Or   I'd   have   no   one   to

love! _____

love! _____

ritard.

THAT'S LOVE

Music & Lyrics by
LEW BROWN and RAY HENDERSON

on a fence__ say, "We're in love,__ so let's com - mence."

La - dies__ and gen - tle - men,__ That's Love!__

__ And when a mar - ried cou - ple

have - n't__ a pot, And still keep sing - ing,

THERE I GO DREAMING AGAIN

Music & Lyrics by
LEW BROWN and RAY HENDERSON

THIS IS THE MRS.

Music & Lyrics by
LEW BROWN and RAY HENDERSON

THE THRILL IS GONE

Music & Lyrics by
LEW BROWN and RAY HENDERSON

TO KNOW YOU IS TO LOVE YOU

Music & Lyrics by B.G. DeSYLVA,
LEW BROWN and RAY HENDERSON

TRY TO REMEMBER

Lyrics by TOM JONES

Music by HARVEY SCHMIDT

1. Try To Re - mem - ber the kind of Sep - tem - ber when
2. Try To Re - mem - ber when life was so ten - der that
3. Deep in De - cem - ber it's nice to re - mem - ber al -

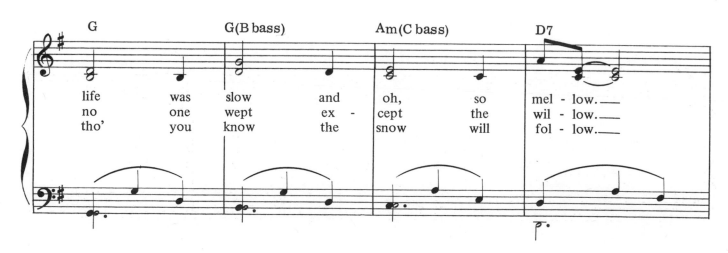

life was slow and oh, so mel - low.___
no one wept ex - cept the wil - low.___
tho' you know the snow will fol - low.___

THE VARSITY DRAG

Music & Lyrics by B.G. DeSYLVA,
LEW BROWN and RAY HENDERSON

an-swer the call when your pro-fes - sor cries: "Ev - 'ry-bod - y

down on the heels, Up on the toes, Stay af - ter school,

Learn how it goes, Ev - 'ry-bod - y do The Var - si - ty

Drag."

WISH YOU WERE HERE

Music & Lyrics by
HAROLD ROME

WOULDN'T IT BE LOVERLY

Lyrics by ALAN JAY LERNER

Music by FREDERICK LOEWE

WITHOUT LOVE

Music & Lyrics by B. G. DeSYLVA,
LEW BROWN and RAY HENDERSON

YOUNG AND FOOLISH

Lyrics by ARNOLD B. HORWITT

Music by ALBERT HAGUE

care - free days, the sun - lit days go by.

Soon e - nough the blue - bird has to fly.

We were fool - ish,

One day we fell in love. Now we

You're The Cream In My Coffee

Music & Lyrics by B.G. DeSYLVA,
LEW BROWN and RAY HENDERSON

Chorus: You're The Cream In My Cof - fee, You're the salt in my stew, You will al - ways be my ne - ces - si - ty, I'd be lost with - out you. You're the starch in my

YOU CAN MAKE MY LIFE A BED OF ROSES

Music & Lyrics by
LEW BROWN and *RAY HENDERSON*

Lyrics:

You Can Make My Life A Bed Of Ros - es, Or
You can have me go - ing to the dev - il, And

make it like a so - ur ap - ple tree, Oh!
with you what an an - gel I could be, So

I'll sup - ply the lit - tle these and
if you want to keep me on the

1.
thos - es, Mar - ry me!

2.
lev - el, Mar - ry me! My heart just pounds in

rum - ba rhy - thm all the day through, __ It on - ly goes back

in - to waltz time when I'm with you. __

You can e - ven have me rub-bing nos - es With fish down at the bot-tom of the

sea, Or You Can Make My Life A Bed Of

Ros - es, Mar - ry Me!

COLLEGE RHYTHM

Lyrics by MACK GORDON

Music by HARRY REVEL

THE EXODUS SONG

Lyrics by PAT BOONE

Music by ERNEST GOLD

see a land where chil-dren can run free. So

take my hand and walk this land with me, And

walk this {love - ly / gold - en} land with me. Tho' I am

just a man,____ When you are by my side, With the

help of God I know I can be strong. So

strong To make this land our home, If

I must fight, I'll fight to make this land our own. Un-

til I die this land is mine!

COME TO ME

Music & Lyrics by B. G. DeSYLVA,
LEW BROWN and RAY HENDERSON

DID YOU EVER SEE A DREAM WALKING?

Lyrics by MACK GORDON

Music by HARRY REVEL

DON'T LET IT BOTHER YOU

Lyrics by MACK GORDON

Music by HARRY REVEL

turn that frown up - side down and smile and sing la de de da da.

Don't Let It Both - er You___ if skies are grey, Learn to grin, take it on the chin,

Ev - 'ry - thing will be o - kay!

sfz

FROM THE TOP OF YOUR HEAD
TO THE TIP OF YOUR TOES

Music & Lyrics by
MACK GORDON and HARRY REVEL

tip of your toes___ you're won-der-ful,_____ You're the

hit of the show,___ you're the cam-e-o of love-li___ness.

Oh, what eyes___ you have, Oh, what lips___ you have,

Oh, what love-ly fea-tures. Talk a-bout a-dor-a-ble

FUNNY GIRL

Lyrics by BOB MERRILL

Music by JULE STYNE

GEORGY GIRL

Lyrics by JIM DALE

Music by TOM SPRINGFIELD

Geor - gy Girl, —
1. Why do all the boys just pass you by?
2. Dream - ing of the some - one you could be.

Could it be you just don't try, or is it the clothes you wear? —
Life is a re - al - i - ty, you can't al - ways run a - way. —

You're al - ways win - dow shop - ping but
Don't be so scared of chang - ing and

nev - er stop - ping to buy.
re - ar - rang - ing your - self.

So, shed those
It's time for

dow - dy feath - ers and fly }
jump - ing down — from the shelf }

a lit - tle bit.

Hey there!— Geor-gy Girl,— There's an-oth-er Geor-gy deep in-side. Bring out all the love you hide and oh, what a change there'd be,—— The world would see a new— Geor-gy Girl. Girl. A new Geor-gy

GIGI

Lyrics by ALAN JAY LERNER

Music by FREDERICK LOEWE

stand - ing up too close, or back too far? _____ When did your

spar - kle turn to fi - re And your warmth be - come de - si - re? Oh, what

mir - a - cle has made you the way you are?

Gi - gi, am I a fool with - out a mind or have I

mere - ly been too blind to re - al - ize? Oh, Gi - gi, why you've been

GOOD MORNING GLORY

Lyrics by MACK GORDON

Music by HARRY REVEL

GOODNIGHT, LOVELY LITTLE LADY

Lyrics by MACK GORDON

Music by Harry Revel

I WISH I WERE ALADDIN

Music & Lyrics by
MACK GORDON and **HARRY REVEL**

IT ALL DEPENDS ON YOU

Music & Lyrics by B. G. DeSYLVA,
LEW BROWN and RAY HENDERSON

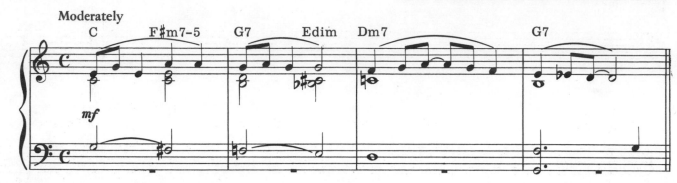

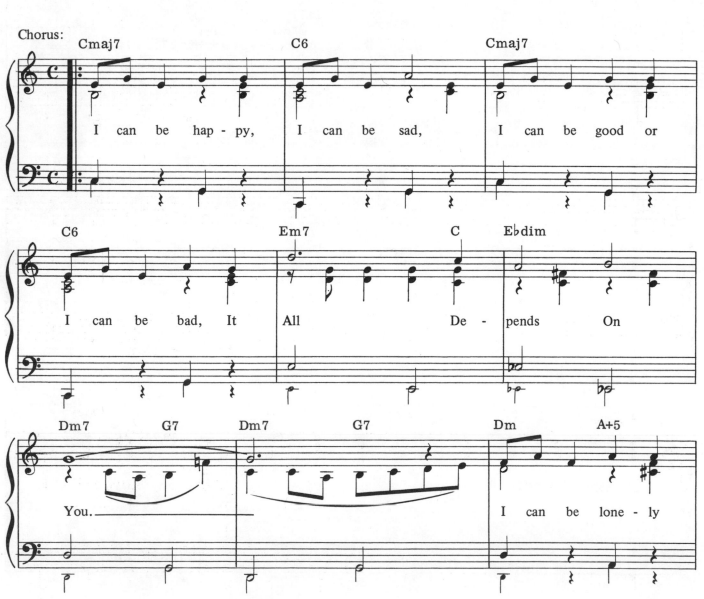

ONCE IN A BLUE MOON

Music & Lyrics by
MACK GORDON and *HARRY REVEL*

clar - ing, "I love you, Oh, will you be mine?

Say you'll be mine." Once In A Blue Moon

some-one like you hap-pens a - long, A bless-ing from heav - en a -

bove, Here am I, here are you, This is love!

bove, Here am I, here are you, This is love!

IF I HAD A TALKING PICTURE OF YOU

Music & Lyrics by B. G. DeSYLVA,
LEW BROWN and RAY HENDERSON

(I'M A DREAMER) AREN'T WE ALL

Music & Lyrics by AL JOLSON, B. G. DeSYLVA,
LEW BROWN and RAY HENDERSON

LOOKIE-LOOKIE-LOOKIE HERE COMES COOKIE

Music & Lyrics by
MACK GORDON

LOVE THY NEIGHBOR

Lyrics by MACK GORDON

Music by HARRY REVEL

MANY MOONS AGO

Lyrics by MACK GORDON

Music by HARRY REVEL

Man - y nights have passed,— Man - y dawns have red - dened and paled,—

Our love was a light— that nev - er

failed. For you're with me now—

liv - ing up to ev - 'ry vow,— And our love is great - er

yet than when we met so Man - y Moons A - go.

ritard.

MAY I ?

Lyrics by MACK GORDON

Music by HARRY REVEL

PARIS IN THE SPRING

Music & Lyrics by
MACK GORDON and HARRY REVEL

STAY AS SWEET AS YOU ARE

Music & Lyrics by
MACK GORDON and HARRY REVEL

SUNNY SIDE UP

Music & Lyrics by B.G. DeSYLVA,
LEW BROWN and RAY HENDERSON

TWO FOR TONIGHT

Music & Lyrics by
MACK GORDON and HARRY REVEL

Lyrics:

This world be-longs to

Two For To-night,— Birds sing their songs to Two For To-night,—

Flow-ers with dew on them, Fra-grance of you on them, They're yours, they're

mine. Moon-beams on high for Two For To-night,—

TAKE A NUMBER FROM ONE TO TEN

Music & Lyrics by
MACK GORDON and HARRY REVEL

TRUE LOVE

Music & Lyrics by
COLE PORTER

Love. For you and I have a guard - ian

an - gel on high with noth - ing to do ____

____ But to give to you and to give to

me Love for - ev - er

true. _____ I true. _____ _____

ritard. e dim. *p*

WITHOUT A WORD OF WARNING

Music & Lyrics by
MACK GORDON and HARRY REVEL

me. With-out A Word Of Warn-ing, and strange as it

seems, We kissed and with that kiss you in-vad-ed my

dreams. I don't know how it hap-pened, but

out of the blue up a- bove You came a-long to

an-swer my song of love. With-

YOU'RE MY PAST, PRESENT AND FUTURE

Lyrics by MACK GORDON

Music by HARRY REVEL

I see my fu-ture, You at my side, A groom and a bride, A home with room for more than two. My be-lov-ed one, You are my past, my pres-ent and my fu-ture, I'm on-ly liv-ing just for you!

WISHING

Music & Lyrics by B.G. DeSYLVA

WITH MY EYES WIDE OPEN I'M DREAMING

Music & Lyrics by
MACK GORDON and HARRY REVEL

(YOU'VE GOT ME)
PICKIN' PETALS OFF O'DAISIES

Music & Lyrics by B.G. DeSYLVA,
LEW BROWN and RAY HENDERSON